Contents

When I was a baby............4

My sister........................8

My brother....................10

We are going to live in a new house ...

because our house is too small.

It was not too small when
I was a baby ...

because then there were only three of us.

Mum

Dad

me

Mum and Dad had this room ...

and I had this one.

It was not too small when my sister was born ...

me

sister

because she came in with me.

sister

brother

me

But then our brother was born.

He will need a big
bed soon.

There is no room for a big bed in here.

And there is no room for a big bed in here.

That is why our house is too small ...

and we are going to live
in a new one.

Dad

Mum

brother

sister

me